Extensive and Varied Exercise Sets	An abundant collection of exercises is included in an exercise set at the end of each section. Exercises are organized within categories. Your instructor will usually provide guidance on which exercises to work. The exercises in the first category, Practice Exercises, follow the same order as the section's worked examples.	The parallel order of the Practice Exercises lets you refer to the worked examples and use them as models for solving these problems.	408
Practice Plus Problems	This category of exercises contains more challenging problems that often require you to combine several skills or concepts.	It is important to dig in and develop your problem-solving skills. Practice Plus Exercises provide you with ample opportunity to do so.	409

③ Review for Quizzes and Tests

Feature	Description	Benefit	Page
Mid-Chapter Check Points	At approximately the midway point in the chapter, an integrated set of review exercises allows you to review the skills and concepts you learned separately over several sections.	By combining exercises from the first half of the chapter, the Mid-Chapter Check Points give a comprehensive review before you move on to the material in the remainder of the chapter.	433
Chapter Review Grids	Each chapter contains a review chart that summarizes the definitions and concepts in every section of the chapter. Examples that illustrate these key concepts are also included in the chart.	Review this chart and you'll know the most important material in the chapter!	459-461
Chapter Review Exercises	A comprehensive collection of review exercises for each of the chapter's sections follows the review grid.	Practice makes perfect. These exercises contain the most significant problems for each of the chapter's sections.	461-464
Chapter Tests	Each chapter contains a practice test with approximately 25 problems that cover the important concepts in the chapter. Take the practice test, check your answers, and then watch the Chapter Test Prep Video CD to see worked-out solutions for any exercises you miss.	You can use the chapter test to determine whether you have mastered the material covered in the chapter.	465
Chapter Test Prep Video CDs	These video CDs found at the back of your text contain worked-out solutions to every exercise in each chapter test.	The videos let you review any exercises you miss on the chapter test.	465
Cumulative Review Exercises	Beginning with Chapter 2, each chapter concludes with a comprehensive collection of mixed cumulative review exercises. These exercises combine problems from previous chapters and the present chapter, providing an ongoing cumulative review.	Ever forget what you've learned? These exercises ensure that you are not forgetting anything as you move forward.	466

MORE TOOLS FOR YOUR
MATHEMATICS SUCCESS

College Algebr

Student Study Pack

Get math help when YOU need it! The Student Study Pack provides you with the ultimate set of support resources to go along with your text. The Student Study Pack can be packaged with your textbook, and contains these invaluable tools:

✔ **Student Solutions Manual**

A printed manual containing full solutions to odd-numbered textbook exercises.

✔ **Prentice Hall Math Tutor Center**

Tutors provide one-on-one tutoring for any problem with an answer at the back of the book. You can contact the Tutor Center via a toll-free phone number, fax, or email.

✔ **CD-ROM Lecture Series**

A comprehensive set of textbook-specific CD-ROMs containing short video clips of the textbook objectives being reviewed and key examples being solved.

Tutorial and Homework Options

MYMATHLAB

MyMathLab can be packaged with your textbook. It is a complete online multimedia resource to help you succeed in learning. MyMathLab features:

✔ The entire textbook online.

✔ Problem-solving video clips and practice exercises, correlated to the examples and exercises in the text.

✔ Online tutorial exercises with guided examples.

✔ Online homework and tests.

✔ Generates a personalized study plan based on your test results.

✔ Tracks all online homework, tests, and tutorial work you do in MyMathLab gradebook.